The Lucky Penny

by Dina McClellan
Illustrated by Cary Pillo

SCHOLASTIC INC.

New York   Toronto   London   Auckland   Sydney
Mexico City   New Delhi   Hong Kong

It was a great day for the park.
Jim had it all planned out.

"First we swim," he said.
"Then we eat. I brought some
good things to nibble on. After
that we can play paddle ball."

Ricky wanted to come, too, but Mom said "No." She wanted him to stay home and rest. Ricky had a cold and a sniffle.

There are three of us—Ricky, Jim, and me. Ricky is the little one. He has a dimple when he smiles.

Jim is the biggest. He thinks he knows it all.

I'm in the middle. My name is Jill.

Jim got our pool passes and our towels.

"We need to take two buses," he said.

"Do you have any money?"

I grabbed my backpack and made it jingle.
I had a lot of dimes. I had a lot of nickels.
I had—no pennies.

No pennies!

"Oh no!" I groaned. "My lucky penny! It's
lost!"

I checked again. And again.

"Wait, Jim!" I called. "We can't go yet. My lucky penny is lost!"

"Are you sure?" said Jim. "It must be there."

"It is not," I said. "I looked twice. This is where I always keep it. It's lost."

Jim put his bag down. "Then let's find it," he said.

"*I'll* find it," said Ricky. "I'm the best at finding things."

If you know me, you know about my bright, shiny, lucky penny. It has always brought me good luck.

I take it with me every day.

My lucky penny never lets me down.

Here's one example.

I had my penny at the school play. Even though we got there late, we got good seats. Ricky and I sat right in front.

Here's another example.

I had my penny at the math test.

Even though the test was hard, it seemed simple.

I got ten out of ten right.

And here's another example.

I had my penny at the Dog Show.

Even though Sparkle would not *sit*, we were the winners. We got first place.

But where was my penny now?

"I bet I know where it is," said Jim.
He rushed to the front room. Ricky was
right behind him. "Lots of things get lost
down here." Jim said. He picked up a
pillow from the couch.

Ricky zoomed across the room. He darted in front of Jim. Then Ricky threw pillows all over the place. "Here, penny, penny! Where are you, penny?" he yelled.

Jim and I started to giggle. Ricky looked at us with a big grin. "Hey!" he said.

"Look what I've got!"

"That's the way to go, Ricky!" I shouted.

I ran over to get my lucky penny.

It wasn't my penny, though. It was a
part of a jigsaw puzzle.

"Wow!" said Jim. "That's been lost for
weeks."

"Good old Ricky," said Ricky.

"It's from the puzzle Uncle Bill brought me," said Jim. "I didn't know where it could be. Thanks, Ricky. Now that puzzle won't be such a mess."

"Yes," said Ricky. "Lucky lucky."

It *was* lucky. But where was my penny?

"I bet I know where it is," said Jim.
He walked over to the table. There was a
pile of things on top. I always put my
odds and ends there. Jim started to look
through the jumble.

He picked up a rattle and gave it a
shake.

"Mine!" said Ricky. He grabbed the
rattle. Then he threw it down.
Ricky looked at the pile on the table.
Then his face lit up. He started to play.
Things went flying around in a wild
scramble.

"Here, penny, penny! Where are you,
penny?" he yelled.

Jim and I started to giggle again.
Ricky looked at us with a big grin.

"Hey!" he said. "Look what I've got!"

"Okay Ricky!" I shouted. I ran over to get my lucky penny. It wasn't my penny, though. It was a baseball card. Ricky brought it over. He made a little bow. I took the card from him and looked at it.

"Wow!" I said. It wasn't just any old card.

It was Dan Maple, my best baseball card. "Thanks, Ricky," I said. "That's been lost for weeks. I didn't know where it was. That card is hard to get."

"Yes," said Ricky. "Lucky lucky."

It *was* lucky. But where was my penny?

"I bet I know where it is," said Jim.

He picked up the end of the rug.

He peeked under it. There was just fluff and dust. Then he picked up the other end.

Ricky zoomed over. Jim and I got out of his way. We had to move fast. Ricky slid under the rug. All we could see was a bump.

"Wiggle wiggle," said the bump. Ricky was having fun. "Here, penny, penny! Where are you, penny?" he yelled.

Jim and I started to giggle again.

Ricky looked at us with a big grin. "Hey!" he said. "Look what I've got!"

"Thanks, Ricky!" I shouted. I ran over to get my lucky penny. It wasn't my penny, though. It was a little key.

I had never seen it. Jim had never seen it.

But Ricky was all grins. He waved the key around in the air.

"*My* key," he said. "My key for my best red box. Come on, Jim! Come on, Jill! Let's get my box."

"Now we can see what's in it," said Jim. "That box has been shut for a year."

"Yes," said Ricky. "Lucky lucky."

It *was* lucky. But where was my penny?

Ricky ran to his room. Jim and I were right behind him. Ricky ran to the table by his bed.

He had lots of boxes there. Big ones, little ones, beautiful ones, ugly ones! He picked up the box in front. It was red and had a gold handle.

"I put the key here," said Ricky. "Then I do this. Then it goes click. And now I lift up the lid. . . ."

"Hey!" said Ricky. "Look what I've got!"
And there in the box was—a penny!

It wasn't my penny, though. It was just an old, dull penny.

Then Mom came in. We told her about looking for my lucky penny. Jim told her about the places we looked. I told her about the lost things we got back. Ricky told her he felt fine. And right then, it started to rain.

"Lucky you stayed home," said Mom.

That's the end of the story.

I never did find that lucky penny.

But you know what?

I didn't need it, after all.

Phonics Booster 35

-le	-s	-es
dimple	dimes	boxes
giggle	ends	buses
handle	grins	passes
jingle	nickels	
jumble	odds	
little	pillows	
Maple	places	
middle	things	
nibble	weeks	
paddle		
puzzle		
rattle		
scramble		
simple		
sniffle		
Sparkle		
table		
Uncle		
wiggle		

★ Words to Remember ★

brought   example   front   though

★ Story Words ★

hey   ones   pennies   towels   threw   winners

24